Explode The Code 6

Nancy Hall
Rena Price

P9-DME-934

out

law

outlaw

Educators Publishing Service, Inc.
Cambridge, Mass. 02138

Text illustrations by Laura Price and Alan Price.

October, 1997 Printing

CONTENTS

Lesson 1

ar says /är/ as in st**ar**.

Read, write, and X it.

1.	car car		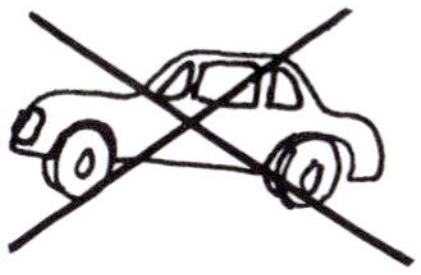	
2.	farm farm			
3.	card Card			
4.	yarn yarn		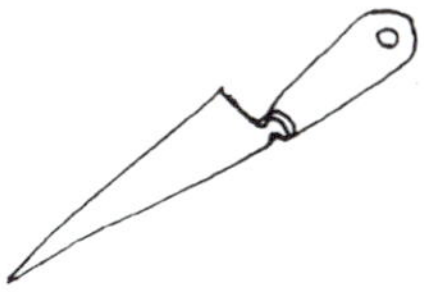	
5.	scarf Scarf	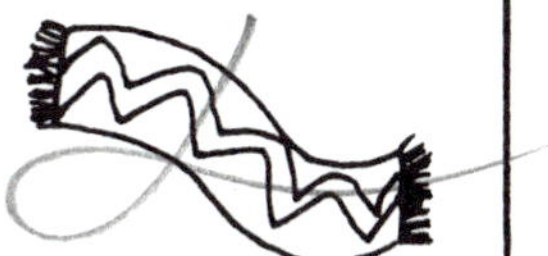	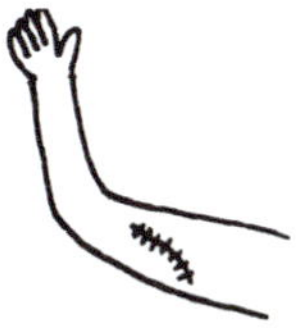	
6.	mark mark			
7.	sparks Sparks			

ar says /är/ as in st**ar**.

◯ it.

(cart) or cat?	date or dart?
march or match?	shark or shack?
happy or harp?	jar or jab?
hard or hand?	smell or snarl?

	Spell.			Write.
1.	(p) b	ai (ar)	(k) h	park
2.	q (c)	(ar) a	f (t)	cart
3.	sh (sc)	an (ar)		scar
4.	(h) n	ar (a)	(m) n	ham
5.	(h) m	(ar) er	(p) t	harp
6.	d (b)	(ar) or	(n) h	barn
7.	sl (sh)	ai (ar)	(k) ke	shark

3

Yes or no?

	Yes	No
1. Can yellow yarn grow longer in the garden?	☐	☒
2. Will a chicken have dinner in the barnyard?	☐	☒
3. Do the stars and planets shine in the daytime?	☐	☒
4. Can a winter scarf be made of candy?	☐	☒
5. Can an army on the hillside see in the darkness?	☒	☐
6. Would it be smart to swim in a sea filled with sharks?	☐	☒
7. Will a market sell milk and eggs and apples to a shopper?	☒	☐

○ it.

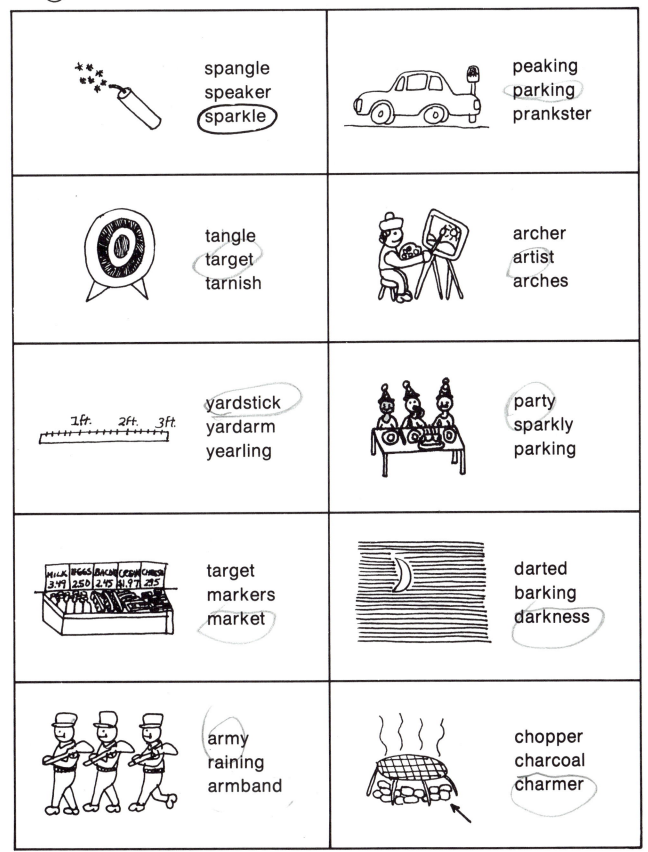

spangle / speaker / (sparkle)	peaking / parking / prankster
tangle / target / tarnish	archer / artist / arches
yardstick / yardarm / yearling	party / sparkly / parking
target / markers / market	darted / barking / darkness
army / raining / armband	chopper / charcoal / charmer

1ft.   2ft.   3ft.

MILK 3.49 EGGS 2.50 BACON 2.45 CREAM 1.97 CHEESE 2.15

Pick the best word to finish each sentence.

carpet   radar   ~~target~~
marble   garden   marching
barnyard   varnish   charcoal

1. In a dart game you throw sharp darts at a _target_ .

2. The band is playing and _marching_ quickly to the music.

3. A fuzzy _carpet_ feels soft on the bottom of your feet.

4. A match starts the _charcoal_ in the grill for hot dogs.

5. If you plant seeds in the _garden_ , tiny plants will grow.

6. He paints _varnish_ on the table to protect it and make it shine.

7. The farmer keeps all the animals in the _barnyard_ .

6

X it.

1.	Marvin throws a marble on the carpet.	☒	
	Marvin keeps a market inside his car.	☐	
2.	The shark swam with a yard of twisted yarn.	☐	
	The shark, dressed in a scarf and bathrobe, sang well.	☒	
3.	The stars sparkle in the darkness.	☐	
	It is hard for Arnold to park cars in the darkness.	☒	
4.	The harp plays music and makes the party lively.	☒	
	The harp plays music and makes the pigpen lively.	☐	
5.	The ants are marching from the garden.	☐	
	The army marches to the biggest target.	☒	
6.	The bandit in the car has many scars.	☒	
	The bandit in the barn has many darts.	☐	
7.	The barking artist is in the barnyard.	☐	
	The artist will varnish his crazy cart.	☒	

Write it, using a word with **ar**.

1. *farm*

2. *yarn*

3. *Shark*

4. *Dart*

5. *Harp*

6. *Car*

7. *Scar*

Lesson 2

or says /ôr/ as in **for**k.

Read, write, and X it.

1.	horn _horn_			
2.	snore _Snore_			
3.	fort _fort_			
4.	thorn _thorn_			
5.	horse _horse_			
6.	porch _porch_			
7.	store _Store_			

or says /ôr/ as in **for**k.

◯ it.

sport or spot?

cork or coat?

shot or short?

north or note?

born or bone?

stork or stock?

can or corn?

stone or storm?

	Spell.			Write.
1.	t (f)	(or) ar	l (k)	_fork_
2.	p (c)	oa (or)	m (n)	_corn_
3.	(th) tr	er (or)	(n) u	_thorn_
4.	ch (c)	or (o)	n (ne)	_cone_
5.	b (t)	(or) oo	ct (ch)	_torch_
6.	s (c)	o (or)	(b) d	_corb_
7.	sh (st)	(or) oa	(m) ne	_storm_

11

Yes or no?

		Yes	No
1.	Will a shortcake get up on a sunny morning?	☐	☒
2.	Can a windy storm begin in a harbor?	☒	☐
3.	Do Barby and a classmate ride horseback in a rowboat?	☐	☒
4.	Can a lazy stork relax on the porch swing?	☐	☒
5.	Can a dark forest be filled with sharp thorns?	☒	☐
6.	Does a razor like to munch on corn at a party?	☐	☒
7.	Can a hornet drive a speeding sports car in the sky?	☐	☒

○ it.

forty **fortress** forgotten	store stormy **story**
recover **record** corner	snoring moaning **morning**
barber **harbor** harder	**forty** frothy lordly
honest horses **hornet**	**shortcake** shorthand shoreline
rather raisin **razor**	shortcut **sports car** sparkler

Pick the best word to finish each sentence.

pork chop	organ	thorny
snort	stores	harbor
corner	forest	shortcake

1. You use both your hands and your feet to play music on the

_____.

2. A horse may _____ when it is running fast.

3. A _____ is a flavorful meat you may have for dinner.

4. There are many big trees in the dark green _____ .

5. A _____ plant will feel sharp if you step on it with bare feet.

6. If you are shopping for a gift, you may visit many

_____.

7. Battleships and other boats can stay for a long time in the

_____.

X it.

1.	The stork will fly north in the spring.	☒	
	The stork sings on the porch.	☐	
2.	A big shortcake was left on the porch.	☐	
	A short rake is used to divide the corn.	☒	
3.	The story tells of a horn on top of the fort.	☒	
	There are forty horses in the store.	☐	
4.	The organ is playing in the harbor.	☐	
	Ugly thorns are growing in the orchard.	☒	
5.	Carl forgot to order a big milk shake.	☐	
	Carl gets a big fork with his shortcake.	☒	
6.	A dark morning is the start of a stormy day.	☒	
	In the morning the children play lots of sports.	☐	
7.	The dark horses are eating with short forks.	☐	
	The sleepy hornet snores on top of the fort.	☒	

Write it, using a word with **or**.

1.		_____
2.		_____
3.		_____
4.		_____
5.		_____
6.		_____
7.		_____

Lesson 3

er, **ir**, and **ur** say /er/ as in
h**er**, b**ir**d, and b**ur**n.

Read, write, and X it.

1. stir
_____

2. curl
_____

3. serve
_____

4. dirt
_____

5. perch
_____

6. skirt
_____

7. nurse
_____

er, **ir**, and **ur** say /er/ as in h**er**, b**ir**d, and b**ur**n.

◯ it.

turn or torn?	fits or first?
jerk or park?	shirt or short?
catch or church?	farm or fern?
porch or perch?	chirp or sharp?

	Spell.			Write.
1.	d b	ur ar	m n	_____
2.	j p	er or	k ch	_____
3.	ch sh	ir or	p t	_____
4.	f t	or ur	u n	_____
5.	th tr	ai ir	b d	_____
6.	b d	ir ea	t b	_____
7.	ch cl	ar ur	th ch	_____

Yes or no?

		Yes	No
1.	Can a person get dirty in a mud puddle?	☐	☐
2.	Can thirty planes land as fast as a shorebird?	☐	☐
3.	Will we be invited to a birthday party for a turtle?	☐	☐
4.	Can hornets sting and hurt if you are teasing them?	☐	☐
5.	Can a stork discover a turnip in the bathtub?	☐	☐
6.	Would you furnish a shack with thirty pink panthers?	☐	☐
7.	Can you see the stars glitter and sparkle when it gets dark?	☐	☐

◯ it.

	numerous nursing nutshell		normal northern noontime
	handle hammer hammock		startle turtle turkey
	third Thursday thorny		morbid mermaid nervy
	thirteen shirtsleeve thirty		backward blackbird blanket
	sorry serpent surprise		thermal thirsty thrifty

Pick the best word to finish each sentence.

purse	shorter	barber
first	thirsty	birthday
ferns	dagger	carport

1.

He may visit a _____ if he needs his curls cut shorter.

2.

When you feel _____, it is a treat to drink water.

3.

A _____ can hold cash and lipstick.

4.

The fastest horse will win the _____ prize.

5.

A turtle has a much _____ tail than a tiger.

6.

At a _____ party the presents are a surprise.

7.

The forest has many leafy, green _____ growing in it.

X it.

1.
Lord Peter likes to perch in the birdbath. ☐

Lord Peter gave the purse to the birds. ☐

2.
The mermaid has curly hair and a skirt. ☐

The mermaid has dirty yarn on her shirt. ☐

3.
The turtle has a surprise on its shell. ☐

The turtle turns the prize on the shelf. ☐

4.
The church has ferns growing from the steeple. ☐

Doris picks ferns growing in the forest. ☐

5.
Gordon gets a surprise from the quick serpent. ☐

Gordon gets a surprise from the squirting hose. ☐

6.
The blackbirds are perching on the scarlet barn. ☐

The blackbirds are pecking at the birdbath. ☐

7.
The nursery has a furry carpet by the crib. ☐

The nurse will serve a big cake for her birthday. ☐

Write it, using a word with **er**, **ir**, or **ur**.

1. _____

2. _____

3. _____

4. _____

5. _____

6. _____

7. _____

Lesson 4

	wor says /wer/ as in **wor**k. Read, write, and X it.		
1.	word _____			
2.	worm _____			
3.	world _____			
	war says /wor/ as in **war**m. Read, write, and X it.		
4.	war _____			
5.	wart _____			
6.	warm _____			

wor says /wer/ as in **wor**k.

◯ it.

| worth or porch? | snored or world? |
| worry or stormy? | word or work? |

war says /wor/ as in **war**m.

◯ it.

| swarm or smart? | warm or mark? |
| award or awake? | harm or warn? |

	Spell.					Write.
1.	w	n	ar	or	t	k	_____
2.	w	n	or	ee	d	b	_____
3.	u	w	or	ar	n	m	_____
4.	m	w	oa	or	lt	ld	_____
5.	w	m	or	ar	n	nt	_____
6.	sw	w	ar	ir	m	n	_____
7.	m	w	ea	ar	d	t	_____

Yes or no?

	Yes	No
1. Can a happy worm sing and warble a song?	☐	☐
2. If you work hard and train to run quickly, could you win the award?	☐	☐
3. Will a person do homework in the middle of a swarm of bees?	☐	☐
4. Is it worthwhile to have a warning of a storm before it strikes?	☐	☐
5. Are you likely to see a hammer and nails on a workbench?	☐	☐
6. Does a snowman have a warm nose and five fingers?	☐	☐
7. Can the world travel backwards if you ask it to?	☐	☐

28

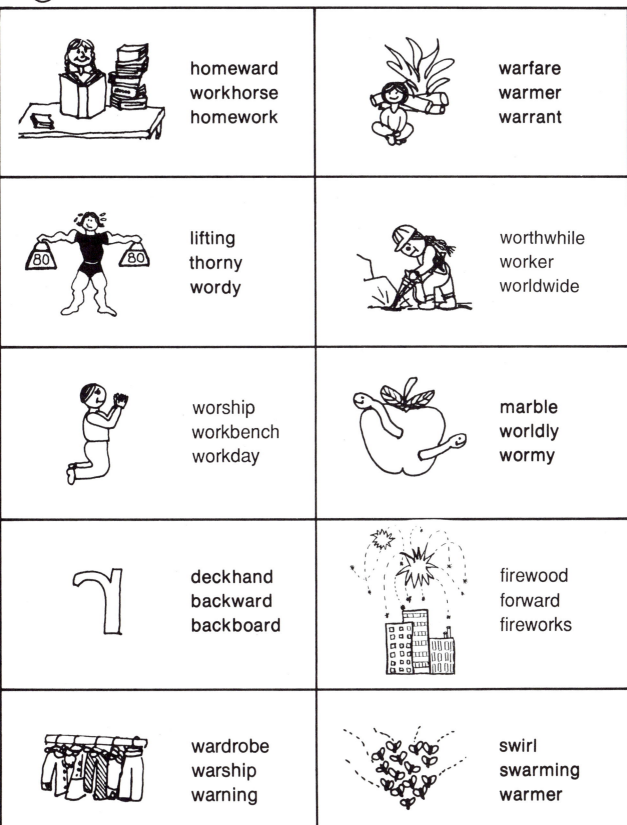

homeward workhorse **homework**	warfare warmer warrant
lifting thorny wordy	worthwhile **worker** worldwide
worship workbench workday	marble worldly **wormy**
deckhand backward backboard	firewood forward **fireworks**
wardrobe warship warning	swirl **swarming** warmer

Pick the best word to finish each sentence.

worry	swarming	warning
workhorse	worship	workbench
warm	homework	award

1. A _____ pulls the hay wagon for the farmer at harvest time.

2. Every week they sing and pray at their place of _____ .

3. It is _____ in the summer when the sun shines a long time.

4. Winning an _____ shows you did the best work on a project.

5. When I am sailing, I _____ about storm warnings.

6. The honeybees were _____ as they left the hive.

7. We study carefully in order to do our _____ well.

X it.

#			
1.	Chuck spells the list of words and gets the award.	☐	
	Chuck can smell the worms in the warm garden.	☐	
2.	Margo warns us to watch for a swarm of bees.	☐	
	Margo warns us to wait for a warm day to swim.	☐	
3.	The worst bandit became a toad with warts.	☐	
	The worst bandit and the dragon are at war.	☐	
4.	The password gets Shirley inside the workshop.	☐	
	The patchwork quilt helps Shirley win the award.	☐	
5.	The blackbird can warble from the treetop.	☐	
	The blackjack player is warning a pal about the trick.	☐	
6.	That workhorse is the shortest in the world.	☐	
	That workbench has a worm inside it.	☐	
7.	Carl got the award for the worst sports car.	☐	
	Carl worked to make a grand shortcake.	☐	

Write it, using a word with **wor** or **war**.

1.		_____
2.		_____
3.		_____
4.		_____
5.		_____
6.		_____
7.		_____

Lesson 5   Review Lesson

Read, write, and X it.

1.	acorn			
2.	barking			
3.	corner			
4.	warning			
5.	birchbark			
6.	serpent			
7.	burst			

◯ it.

beaver or beard?

further or furnish?

squared or squirted?

burner or barnyard?

border or worker?

radar or reader?

30

thirty or thorny?

platter or platform?

34

	Spell.		Write.
1.	car cor	pet port	_____
2.	bird dirt	bash bath	_____
3.	fan lan	tern torn	_____
4.	stor slar	vy y	_____
5.	mom mon	stare ster	_____
6.	fun sun	burn barn	_____
7.	cor car	ner mar	_____

Yes or no?

	Yes No
1. Will a beaver furnish its home with a lantern?	☐ ☐
2. Can you read a story that tells of a mean monster and a brave hero?	☐ ☐
3. Does a serpent travel with a scarf and turtleneck shirt?	☐ ☐
4. Will robins be chirping and splashing in the birdbath in March?	☐ ☐
5. Do the actors in a play stand and speak from a platform?	☐ ☐
6. Can a paper clip get a sunburn on a sandy beach?	☐ ☐
7. Is it fun to box and spar with a porcupine and a panther?	☐ ☐

○ it.

	brushes bursting burden		dirt direct duress
	charming snorkel charcoal		fort forbid forecast
	quicksand whirlwind worthwhile		morsel snoring nursing
	alarm larder aloft		wormhole worldwide workweek
	pattern panther partner		turtle fertile fortune

Pick the best word to finish each sentence.

porcupine	swarming	paper clip
fingernails	fortune	birchbark
remark	actor	turtleneck

1. The _____ puts on a costume for the play.

2. On your hands you have ten _____, which can get dirty.

3. The teacher uses a _____ to keep homework papers together.

4. A _____ has sharp quills, which can hurt your skin.

5. The bees are _____ around the new hive as we approach.

6. A sweater may have a _____ to help keep your neck snug and warm.

7. A birch tree is covered with _____, which protects it as it grows.

X it.

1.	The mummy needs to cut his long fingernails.	☐	
	The mummy puts his thirteen fingers on the trombone.	☐	
2.	King Arthur is surprised by the fortune in the trunk.	☐	
	King Arthur is surprised by the truck in the fortress.	☐	
3.	A serpent has a picnic by the birdbath.	☐	
	The birds like to picnic on the bathtub.	☐	
4.	In the play, the actor is barking like a dog.	☐	
	The actor in the play is working in darkness.	☐	
5.	Inside the lantern in the park there is an acorn.	☐	
	In the park the actor is swinging the lantern.	☐	
6.	At home the girls are reading a story on the carpet.	☐	
	The girls squirted the garden with the long hose.	☐	
7.	The porcupine gets the award at the party.	☐	
	The beaver sets the alarm in the corner.	☐	

Write it.

1.		_____
2.		_____
3.		_____
4.		_____
5.		_____
6.		_____
7.		_____

Lesson 6

igh says /ī/ as in light.
The gh is silent.

Read, write, and X it.

1.	fight			
2.	night			
3.	high			
4.	sight			
5.	bright			
6.	fright			
7.	tight			

igh says /ī/ as in **ligh**t.

◯ it.

flight or fit?

high or highness?

sigh or sight?

tight or tiger?

right or rush?

midnight or midway?

frighten or fighter?

tighten or twilight?

	Spell.			Write.
1.	f h	ee igh	t d	_____
2.	k l	igh ai	m t	_____
3.	m n	oa igh	b t	_____
4.	sh t	ir igh	t r	_____
5.	br b	igh ea	t f	_____
6.	fr tr	igh i	k t	_____
7.	sw s	ai igh	t n	_____

Yes or no?

		Yes	No
1.	Can you drive a sports car on a highway at twilight?	☐	☐
2.	Can you sleep overnight on a bunk bed?	☐	☐
3.	Is a flashlight brighter than a candle?	☐	☐
4.	Does lightning in a storm frighten you a lot?	☐	☐
5.	Will sunlight shine warmly at midnight?	☐	☐
6.	Are you right to say ten plus ten is sixteen?	☐	☐
7.	Is a windmill on a farm higher than an anthill?	☐	☐

○ it.

	midship midyear midnight
	tighten tigress Titanic
	fighting fainting frighten
	flight deck flashlight flashback
	sunlight delight sublime
	spotless spotlight sportscast
	tigerish lightbulb tightrope
	brightness bribery bridesmaid
	lightest lightning lively
	deliver delight insight

Pick the best word to finish each sentence.

lightning	tightrope	brightest
flight	right	flashlight
night	highness	sigh

1.

The acrobat rides a bike on a high _____ .

2.

During a storm there is sometimes thunder and

_____ with rain.

3.

We get up in the morning and go to bed at _____ .

4.

Do you make a wish when you are the first to see the

_____ star of the night?

5.

If it is dark at midnight, you may need a _____ .

6.

Do not turn left, turn _____ .

7.

After a long _____ , the airplane landed in
Nome, Alaska.

X it.

1.
The sports car is going north on the highway. ☐

The short cat is sneaking to a higher branch. ☐

2.
Her highness will light the lantern. ☐

The selfish little girl has a light bundle. ☐

3.
The sky is bright with sunlight. ☐

The lightning brightens the sky. ☐

4.
Mark tightens the ropes on the sailboat. ☐

Mark holds the dog as he slides on the tightrope. ☐

5.
The tiger and the smart girl dine by candlelight. ☐

The smart girl lights a candle on the birthday cake. ☐

6.
The fighter is wishing that he will be a winner. ☐

The goblin with whiskers will frighten the children. ☐

7.
Peter slept overnight in the church steeple. ☐

The bell in the steeple clangs at midnight. ☐

Write it, using a word with **igh**.

1. _____

2. _____

3. _____

4. _____

5. _____

6. _____

7. _____

oo says two things:
Sometimes **oo** says /$\overline{oo}$/ as in b**oo**t.
Sometimes **oo** says /$\overline{oo}$/ as in b**oo**k.

Read, write, and X it.

1.	foot _____			
2.	cook _____			
3.	broom _____			
4.	moon _____			
5.	spoon _____			
6.	roof _____			
7.	goose _____			

oo says /o͞o/ as in b**oo**t.
oo says /o͝o/ as in b**oo**k.

◯ it.

good or goose?

hook or shook?

food or foot?

stool or stoop?

tooth or troop?

mood or moose?

booth or boot?

soot or shoot?

	Spell.			Write.
1.	b d	oo oa	g k	_____
2.	n m	oo oi	n m	_____
3.	st sp	ea oo	k n	_____
4.	br dr	oo oe	k m	_____
5.	g f	o oo	t d	_____
6.	r gr	u oo	t f	_____
7.	g j	or oo	t se	_____

Yes or no?

		Yes	No
1.	Does sandpaper feel smooth in the morning?	☐	☐
2.	Can a poodle catch a football in the dark?	☐	☐
3.	Will a woolly hood keep you warm in winter?	☐	☐
4.	Is it spooky in a dark, wooded forest?	☐	☐
5.	Are you foolish to ride home on a broomstick?	☐	☐
6.	Is a spoonful of root beer a good cure for a sick hamster?	☐	☐
7.	Have you understood this lesson so far?	☐	☐

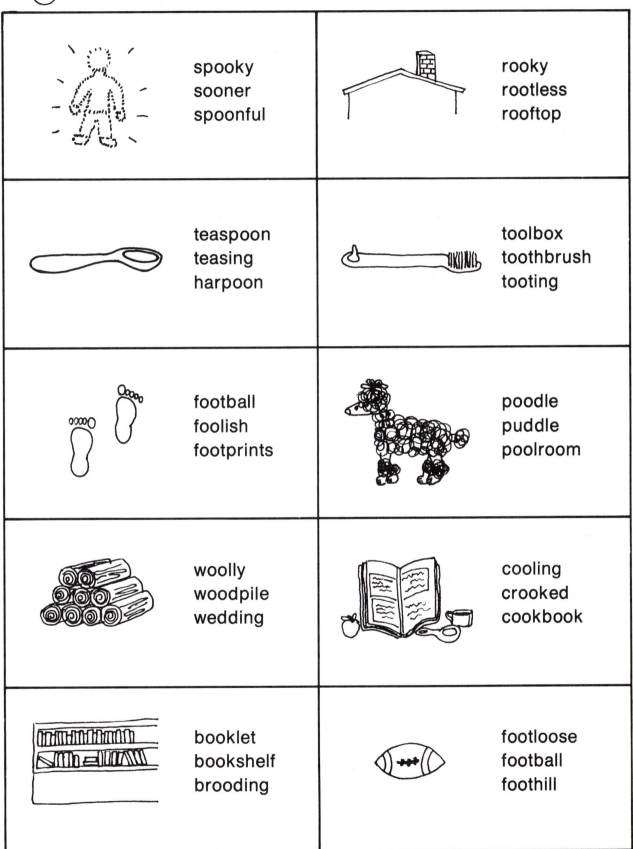

spooky sooner spoonful	rooky rootless rooftop
teaspoon teasing harpoon	toolbox toothbrush tooting
football foolish footprints	poodle puddle poolroom
woolly woodpile wedding	cooling crooked cookbook
booklet bookshelf brooding	footloose football foothill

Pick the best word to finish each sentence.

moose	spooky	toolbox
rooftop	cookbook	understood
toothbrush	goodness	pool

1. When you are fixing supper, you may need to use a

_____.

2. The foolish _____ is eating grass behind the woodpile.

3. On a hot summer day, swimming in a _____ cools me off.

4. The repairer came with a _____ to fix the TV.

5. To keep your teeth clean you must use your

_____ after every meal.

6. The snow on the _____ shines in the bright moonlight.

7. On Halloween, goblins and black cats help make it a very

_____ night!

X it.

1.	The hungry crook is looking for some French food. ☐ The French cook is reading the cookbook. ☐	
2.	The football fell on the crooked rooftop. ☐ The goose stood on the crooked bookshelf. ☐	
3.	Mike is snooping into the chicken coop. ☐ Mike is stooping to look at the footprints. ☐	
4.	The woolly poodle has a boot on its right foot. ☐ The frightened poodle stood and shook as I read the book. ☐	
5.	Betsy understood the textbook. ☐ Betsy inspects the spooky room. ☐	
6.	The foolish groom has a loose tooth. ☐ The fool is stuck in the tiny booth. ☐	
7.	The moose is tooting its horn in the moonlight. ☐ The crazy raccoon is barking at the moose. ☐	

Write it, using a word with **oo**.

1.	_____
2.	_____
3.	_____
4.	_____
5.	_____
6.	_____
7.	_____

Lesson 8

ea says two things:
Sometimes ea says /ē/ as in eat.
Sometimes ea says /ĕ/ as in head.

Read, write, and X it.

1.	feast _____			
2.	thread _____			
3.	sweat _____			
4.	beard _____			
5.	dead _____			
6.	ear _____			
7.	breath _____			

57

ea says /ē/ as in **ea**t.
ea says /ĕ/ as in h**ea**d.

◯ it.

read or ride?

dead or deep?

beads or beard?

spare or spear?

wheat or wealth?

peach or porch?

beast or best?

bread or beard?

		Spell.				Write.
1.		b d	ea oo	st ts	_____
2.		h n	ee ea	p d	_____
3.		br dr	ai ea	m n	_____
4.		dr d	ea i	b d	_____
5.		b p	ar ea	d rd	_____
6.		d b	ea ir	t d	_____
7.		thr th	ir ea	d p	_____

Yes or no?

	Yes No
1. Can a dead beast squeal at a purple turtle?	☐ ☐
2. Do you spread cream on your bread for breakfast?	☐ ☐
3. Can you hear me speaking if you are deaf?	☐ ☐
4. Will a dragon shave its beard with a spear?	☐ ☐
5. Will you go sailing beyond the harbor in bad weather?	☐ ☐
6. When it is very warm and the sun is high, will you sweat?	☐ ☐
7. Does a goose in a meadow have lots of feathers?	☐ ☐

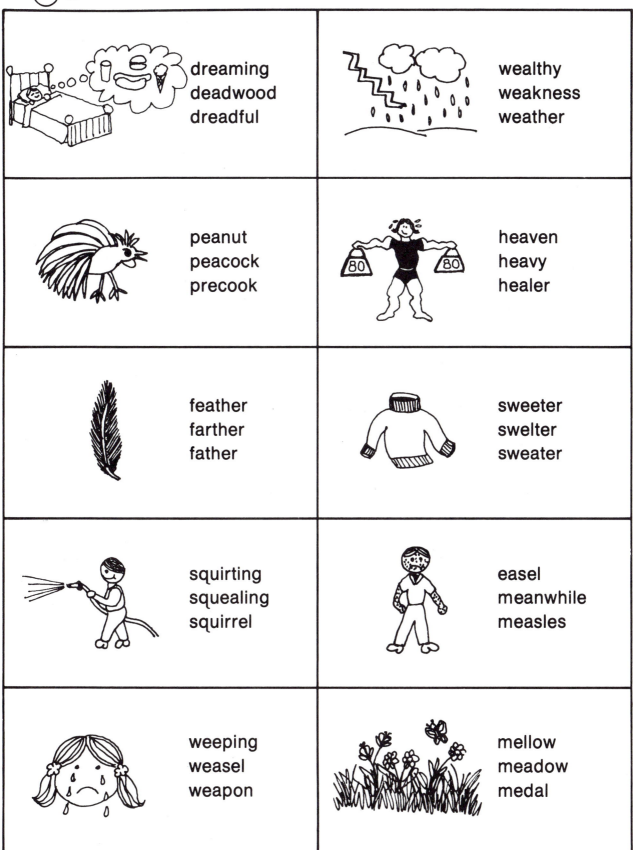

dreaming
deadwood
dreadful

wealthy
weakness
weather

peanut
peacock
precook

heaven
heavy
healer

feather
farther
father

sweeter
swelter
sweater

squirting
squealing
squirrel

easel
meanwhile
measles

weeping
weasel
weapon

mellow
meadow
medal

Pick the best word to finish each sentence.

underneath	sweaty	deaf
meadow	healthy	bread
breath	ears	feathers

1. For a sandwich, she spread peanut butter and jelly on her

   _____.

2. When it is chilly and frosty, you can see the vapor of your

   _____.

3. The team was all hot and _____ after the
   hard football game.

4. In wintertime, you put on a hat and scarf to keep your head and
   _____ warm.

5. When you feel and look fine, the doctor says that you are

   _____.

6. The presents and cards were stacked _____
   the brightly lighted tree.

7. Birds have plenty of _____ to help keep them
   warm.

X it.

1. Tex is reading at the wedding. ☐

   Tex is reaching for his leather billfold. ☐

2. The cat is romping in the pleasant meadow. ☐

   The pheasant is flying in the meadow. ☐

3. The peacock has a flea on its feathered head. ☐

   The peacock spreads its tail feathers. ☐

4. Mark wished that he had as handsome a beard as his pet. ☐

   Mark wished for bread with cheddar cheese. ☐

5. The noose hangs from the tree. ☐

   The moose is dreaming of a cool, shady tree. ☐

6. It is easy to hear that screaming. ☐

   The eagle likes to splash in the stream. ☐

7. David sneaks up behind the beast. ☐

   The beast is stealing David's bread. ☐

Write it, using a word with **ea**.

1.		_____
2.		_____
3.		_____
4.		_____
5.		_____
6.		_____
7.		_____

Lesson 9

ie says two things:
Sometimes **ie** says /ī/ as in p**ie**.
Sometimes **ie** says /ē/ as in police ch**ie**f.

Read, write, and X it.

1.	tie _____			
2.	pie _____			
3.	lie _____			
4.	field _____			
5.	thief _____			
6.	shield _____			
7.	chief _____			

ie says /ī/ as in p**ie**.
ie says /ē/ as in police ch**ie**f.

◯ it.

sheep or shield?

yell or yield?

die or day?

lie or load?

brief or breath?

press or priest?

green or grief?

field or feel?

Spell.   Write.

		Spell.			Write.
1.		gr ch	ei ie	f p	_____
2.		p b	ie ea		_____
3.		h f	ea ie	p d	_____
4.		d t	ie ee		_____
5.		h f	ie a	ld lt	_____
6.		th f	oo ie	th f	_____
7.		ch sh	ie igh	lp ld	_____

67

Yes or no?

	Yes No
1. Can a thief hide a weapon under a sweater?	☐ ☐
2. Can the shortstop eat apple pie in right field?	☐ ☐
3. Can a rainstorm with thunder and lightning be brief?	☐ ☐
4. Does a farmer work in the field with a briefcase?	☐ ☐
5. Can a poodle tie its leash to a woodpile?	☐ ☐
6. Will you serve pie or birthday cake on a silver shield?	☐ ☐
7. Will a fire chief wear leather boots?	☐ ☐

◯ it.

until untie untidy	thief think therefore
pie crust poolside piano	bookcase briefcase breakfast
mischief handkerchief handlebar	father feather fielder
canary campfire camera	nickel tieback necktie
sweeter sweater seized	windmill watershed windshield

Pick the best word to finish each sentence.

windshield	airfield	priest
chiefly	believe	necktie
tied	brief	handkerchief

1. The _____ will pray and worship in the church.

2. When it starts to rain, we turn on the car's
   _____ wipers.

3. Can you tie your own _____ under a shirt collar?

4. The freedom fighters _____ in worldwide freedom.

5. The plane landed with the help of spotlights on the
   _____.

6. When you have a runny nose, you need a
   _____.

7. The captain lowered the sails and _____ the boat to the dock.

X it.

1. The chief is heaving a heavy spear. ☐

   The chief is heaping up the meatballs. ☐

2. The eagle swoops at the windshield. ☐

   The windshield is covered with soot. ☐

3. David ran thirty yards on the football field. ☐

   The healthy baby kicks the ball in the backyard. ☐

4. Ricardo tied his necktie to the flagpole. ☐

   Ricardo tried to make mudpies in the sandbox. ☐

5. The sneaky thief is reaching into the briefcase. ☐

   The thief is hoping to sneak away with the baked goods. ☐

6. Sally waves her handkerchief at the beast. ☐

   Sally drops her paper handkerchief on the beach. ☐

7. In this weather the highway looks like a mudpie. ☐

   Walter makes mudpies at the baseball field. ☐

Write it, using a word with **ie**.

1. _____

2. _____

3. _____

4. _____

5. _____

6. _____

7. _____

72

Lesson 10 Review Lesson

Read, write, and X it.

#				
1.	stool _____			
2.	zoo _____			
3.	leash _____			
4.	hood _____			
5.	stream _____			
6.	high _____			
7.	sweater _____			

◯ it.

shook or sock?	Snoopy or spooky?
sneak or snack?	boost or boots?
stool or tools?	peas or pies?
sigh or sight?	peach or patch?

	Spell.		Write.
1.	neck reck	toe tie	_____
2.	fight foot	print paint	_____
3.	farth feath	est er	_____
4.	tooth tight	brush bush	_____
5.	sweat sweet	ly er	_____
6.	steep stoop	ing ling	_____
7.	Spain spoon	ful fy	_____

75

Yes or no?

		Yes	No
1.	Does a baby goose believe in mermaids?	☐	☐
2.	Will a spook enjoy sightseeing at the zoo?	☐	☐
3.	Do cooks sometimes use leather to make pumpkin pie?	☐	☐
4.	Does Snoopy travel on a broomstick to visit his pals?	☐	☐
5.	Could you order a cone with three scoops?	☐	☐
6.	Does fresh peach pie taste good at the end of a feast?	☐	☐
7.	Will the repairer use tools and a flashlight to fix the leaking pipes?	☐	☐

	footnote foolproof footprints		dashboard flashlight flat-footed
	father farther feather		stooping stopping standing
	daylight limelight moonlight		highness highjack tightness
	sponsor spoonful soothsay		sightless sightseeing slightly
	breadstick bedstand bedspread		beardless breathless beadless

Pick the best word to finish each sentence.

bedspread	mudpies	sightseeing
weather	hood	stooping
moonlight	sweating	sweater

1.

I smoothed the blankets on my bed and then put on the

_____.

2.

We have not yet seen the sights of Atlanta, so we are going

_____.

3.

The athlete is _____ after running six miles.

4.

Jeanie is _____ to pick up the paper she
dropped.

5.

The TV forecasts said the _____ today would
be cool and rainy.

6.

When it is chilly, I pull up the _____ of my
jacket.

7.

My little sister likes to use a shovel in the sandbox and make

_____.

X it.

1.
Snoopy is sightseeing at the zoo. ☐

Snoopy is frightened by the spook. ☐

2.
The crook sneaks into the moonlit room. ☐

The cook speaks to the roomful of nurses. ☐

3.
The breathless fighter slumps in his corner. ☐

The frightened sailor stoops to pick up the beads. ☐

4.
The spook has a leather jacket with a hood. ☐

The feather duster was in front of the TV. ☐

5.
The windmill is higher than the trees. ☐

Her highness stood on top of the broomstick. ☐

6.
The crook scooped the tools into a loose bag. ☐

The cook stacks her pies on the crooked stool. ☐

7.
In the middle of the woods stood a porcupine. ☐

The tin woodman picked a peach and started eating it. ☐

Write it.

1.	
2.	
3.	
4.	
5.	
6.	
7.	

Lesson 11

oi and **oy** say /oy/ as in b**oi**l and b**oy**.
oy comes at the end of a word.

Read, write, and X it.

1.	Roy _____			
2.	joint _____			
3.	join _____			
4.	joy _____			
5.	point _____			
6.	noisy _____			
7.	annoy _____			

oi and **oy** say /oy/ as in b**oi**l and b**oy**.

◯ it.

coy or coin?

bay or boy?

tie or toil?

took or toy?

broom or broil?

destroy or royal?

soil or shoot?

coil or coal?

		Spell.			Write.
1.		f t	oi oy		_____
2.		c p	oi oy	m n	_____
3.		d b	oi oo	k l	_____
4.		f j	oi oy		_____
5.		g j	oi oy	lt nt	_____
6.		d b	oy oo	ch k	_____
7.		p j	oy oi	m n	_____

Yes or no?

		Yes	No
1.	Will the baby be spoiled if he gets lots of toys?	☐	☐
2.	Do you enjoy reading in a room that is messy and noisy?	☐	☐
3.	Can tinfoil be used to keep food fresh and moist?	☐	☐
4.	Is a coin so heavy that a child will drop it?	☐	☐
5.	Will a joyful poodle broil meat on a grill?	☐	☐
6.	Should Roy use a bandage and ointment on a cut?	☐	☐
7.	Would you plant poison ivy in your garden?	☐	☐

engine enjoy jointly	oyster overturn oilskin
painted jointed pointed	soil togs toys
boyish brooding broiling	spoil sprout spool
poison purpose person	pantry destroy royal
joining growling growing	oilcan organize ointment

Pick the best word to finish each sentence.

joint	enjoy	royal
annoy	oily	poison
tinfoil	broiling	destroy

1. Be careful to avoid a bottle that is marked _____ .

2. We use _____ to cover leftovers and keep them moist.

3. You burn charcoal in a grill when _____ hamburgers.

4. An athlete will _____ playing a soccer game with the winning team.

5. Noisy workers in the library will _____ the readers.

6. The bones of the arm form a _____ at the elbow.

7. If you push a heavy snowman over, you _____ it.

X it.

1. Tom pointed at the bright coins by the bread. ☐

   At night Tom points at a bright star that he can see from his bed. ☐

2. The owl is boiling the oil over the campfire. ☐

   The owl joins a noisy gang on a summer night. ☐

3. The boy is spoiling his pet pooch with candy. ☐

   The boy in the sandbox has spoiled the party. ☐

4. She points at the bottle of poison on the shelf. ☐

   The bottle of poison is destroying the shell. ☐

5. The baby has a raccoon that annoys Scott. ☐

   The girl is annoyed by the noisy boy on the train. ☐

6. Jeff enjoys broiling hot dogs for his classmates. ☐

   Jeff joins his dog in the house with the pointed roof. ☐

7. The coins make a fine noise as they hit the pavement. ☐

   The boys pay for the treat with thirteen silver coins. ☐

Write it, using a word with **oi** or **oy**.

1.	_____
2.	_____
3.	_____
4.	_____
5.	_____
6.	_____
7.	_____

Lesson 12

ou and sometimes **ow** say /ou/ as in m**ou**th and c**ow**.

Read, write, and X it.

1.	south _____			
2.	mouse _____			
3.	cow _____			
4.	growl _____			
5.	outside _____			
6.	nightgown _____			
7.	lighthouse _____			

89

ou and sometimes **ow** say /ou/ as in m**ou**th and c**ow**.

◯ it.

round or road?	book or bow?
stool or stout?	coach or couch?
torn or towel?	brown or broom?
loud or lord?	looping or plowing?

		Spell.				Write.
1.		sl cl	ou oo	b d		_____
2.		ow oi	t l			_____
3.		m n	or ou	te th		_____
4.		b d	ow ar	k n		_____
5.		cr ch	oo ow	n u		_____
6.		sh s	oa ou	d th		_____
7.		gl cl	ow oo	m n		_____

91

Yes or no?

		Yes	No
1.	Will a cow get a crown for eating the freshest flowers?	☐	☐
2.	Does a clown act like a fool and jump up and down in the spotlight?	☐	☐
3.	Is a brown mouse as big and heavy as the couch in the living room?	☐	☐
4.	Does the little toy mouse clean your messy house with a broom and towel?	☐	☐
5.	Can you see down to the ground from a lighthouse by the seashore?	☐	☐
6.	Do owls make spooky noises outside at night?	☐	☐
7.	Is it cloudy and damp in the garden during a rain shower?	☐	☐

◯ it.

	topsoil tower towel		founding flounder flouncing
	cower couch course		crooked clouded crowded
	noontime moodiness moonlight		grounded roomed rounded
	shower showman showy		cloudy lower loudest
	founding frowning crowing		foulest floater flower

Pick the best word to finish each sentence.

counted	growling	towel
allow	drowsy	mouthful
found	cloudy	thousand

1. If your cute pet is lost, you are glad when it is finally

   _____.

2. After a shower or swim in the pool, we use a _____ to get dry.

3. The clown felt very _____ when it was past his bedtime.

4. If you have a _____ of food and try to talk, you might choke.

5. On a _____ day you cannot see the bright sunlight.

6. A _____ is a big number that has three zeros at the end.

7. A dog that is _____ can frighten even a brave person.

X it.

1.	Joy looks outside the house at the pile of coins. ☐ Joy looks in the round house for the pile of toys. ☐	
2.	The clown has a squirting flower on her head. ☐ The clown has a squeaking mouse on her head. ☐	
3.	Roy shouts from the lighthouse when it gets cloudy. ☐ Roy plays the trumpet louder than the rest of the crowd. ☐	
4.	The poodle is growling at the brown trout. ☐ The trout by the river frowns at the crowd. ☐	
5.	The cow has a mouthful of ferns for supper. ☐ The couch is covered with a shower of ferns. ☐	
6.	The owl is throwing the crown at the king's throne. ☐ The owl with the crown is perched on the throne. ☐	
7.	The mouse enjoys the noise from the loud bulldozer. ☐ The boy with the hammer is frowning at the loud bulldozer. ☐	

Write it, using a word with **ou** or **ow**.

1. _____

2. _____

3. _____

4. _____

5. _____

6. _____

7. _____

Lesson 13

au and **aw** say /aw/ as in h**au**l and s**aw**.

Read, write, and X it.

1.	paw _____			
2.	lawn _____			
3.	shawl _____			
4.	jaw _____			
5.	hawk _____			
6.	yawn _____			
7.	claw _____			

au and **aw** say /aw/ as in h**au**l and s**aw**.

◯ it.

claw or clay?	Paul or powder?
pow or paw?	found or fawn?
dawn or down?	boil or draw?
auto or howl?	August or awful?

Spell.   Write.

1.	y h	aw ow	t k	_____
2.	br dr	oy aw		_____
3.	cr cl	aw ou	d l	_____
4.	w y	ai aw	m n	_____
5.	st sh	a aw	l mp	_____
6.	h n	au oi	l t	_____
7.	str shr	oy aw		_____

Yes or no?

	Yes	No
1. Can a hawk do its laundry in the birdbath?	☐	☐
2. Do you think Paul enjoys playing on a seesaw on the lawn?	☐	☐
3. Can an auto crawl faster than a grasshopper can hop?	☐	☐
4. Is it helpful to use a lawnmower to trim the grass?	☐	☐
5. Can you polevault with a drinking straw?	☐	☐
6. Is it your fault if you yawn each day in class?	☐	☐
7. Will you squawk if you get coleslaw for supper?	☐	☐

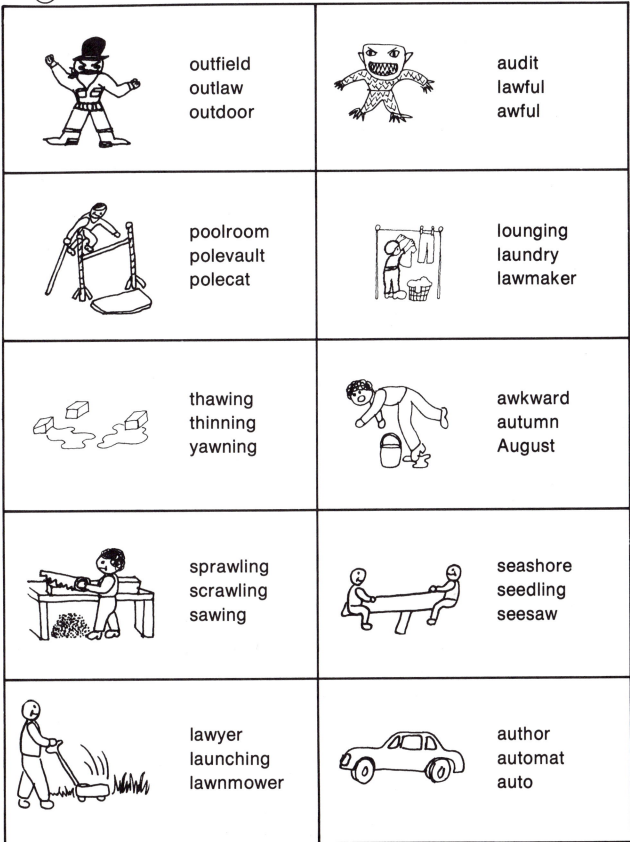

outfield outlaw outdoor	audit lawful awful
poolroom polevault polecat	lounging laundry lawmaker
thawing thinning yawning	awkward autumn August
sprawling scrawling sawing	seashore seedling seesaw
lawyer launching lawnmower	author automat auto

Pick the best word to finish each sentence.

drawing	thawing	yawning
lawnmower	autumn	claws
outlaw	sawing	coleslaw

1. The season when the leaves fall from the trees is

   _____.

2. The lumberjack is _____ up the logs to make boards.

3. In the summer we trim the grass around the house with a

   _____.

4. When I am sleepy, you will see me _____.

5. In the spring when the snow is melting, we say it is

   _____.

6. A person acting outside the law in the old West was called

   an _____.

7. When the eagle saw the food, it used its _____ to pick it up.

X it.

1.	Paul made a drawing of an awful outlaw. ☐ Paul's auto makes an awful noise on the turnpike. ☐	
2.	The moose is sprawling on the lawn. ☐ The moon is spraying moonbeams at the dawn. ☐	
3.	The hawk has its claws on the mouse. ☐ The mouse is crawling up to the author's house. ☐	
4.	Paula is sipping a milk shake with a straw. ☐ The straw is slipping down from the hayloft. ☐	
5.	The lawnmower got tangled with the laundry. ☐ The laundry is flapping in the autumn wind. ☐	
6.	The poodle sinks its jaws into the raw meat. ☐ The snow is melting and thawing into puddles on the lawn. ☐	
7.	The crow is yawning and squawking. ☐ The cow is sprawled in a heap of straw. ☐	

Write it, using a word with **aw**.

1.		_____
2.		_____
3.		_____
4.		_____
5.		_____
6.		_____
7.		_____

ew, **ui**, **ue**, and sometimes **ou** say /o͞o/ as in s**ui**t.

Read, write, and X it.

1.	fruit _____			
2.	group _____			
3.	stew _____			
4.	blew _____			
5.	soup _____			
6.	new _____			
7.	flew _____			

ew, **ui**, **ue**, and sometimes **ou** say /o͞o/ as in s**ui**t.

◯ it.

blue or boo?	news or noise?
yawn or youth?	crowd or cruise?
suit or soup?	screw or stew?
glue or grew?	true or threw?

	Spell.				Write.
1.		z s	ou oi	t p	_____
2.		fr gr	au ui	d t	_____
3.		sh s	ow ui	t p	_____
4.		bl dl	aw ew		_____
5.		gr br	aw ou	q p	_____
6.		ch sh	ew oe		_____
7.		m n	ow ew		_____

Yes or no?

	Yes No
1. Can you eat soup with a long screwdriver?	☐ ☐
2. Will you stew a new suit before you button it?	☐ ☐
3. Do you put glue on a broken toy to fix it?	☐ ☐
4. Do you enjoy playing with a happy group of boys and girls?	☐ ☐
5. Will a short suitcase be put in a sloppy stew?	☐ ☐
6. Can a marble statue chew fruit?	☐ ☐
7. If you bruise and scrape your arm, do you put ointment on it?	☐ ☐

◯ it.

clawing
choosing
chewing

frustrate
fragment
fruitcake

shrewish
screwdriver
shrewd

coiling
cruelly
cruising

wanted
wooded
wounded

strewn
sewed
stewed

bruised
blue jay
bluebell

soothsay
suitcase
suitable

newspaper
newsboy
newsstand

scribble
scrapbook
scarecrow

Pick the best word to finish each sentence.

overdue	statue	cruel
chewing	bluebird	withdrew
suitcase	screwdriver	newspaper

1. When you get ready to go on a trip, you pack your

   _____ .

2. If a screw is loose, you will need a _____
   to fix it.

3. The stone figure in the park is called a _____ .

4. If you see something with lovely blue feathers flying in the sky,

   it may be a _____ .

5. Do you have a _____ delivered to your house
   every morning?

6. If you do not return your book to the library within three weeks, it

   will be _____.

7. The clown is _____ the raw carrot noisily.

X it.

1. The statue drew the drapes in the drawing room. ☐

   The statue has dewdrops all over it. ☐

2. The bluebird flew over the rainbow. ☐

   The rainbow grew fainter and fainter. ☐

3. The group went on a cruise together. ☐

   The goose is cruising on a banana boat. ☐

4. The youth threw the glue in the soup. ☐

   The soup grew too cool for Goldilocks. ☐

5. Sue blew out the birthday candles. ☐

   Sue is holding the chewed fruit. ☐

6. Uncle Lou stoops to pick up his new suit. ☐

   Lou spills soup on his uncle's new suit. ☐

7. The fattest fruit grew on the peach tree. ☐

   A few trees were cut and used to construct a cabin. ☐

Write it, using a word with **ew**, **ui**, or **ou**.

1.		_____ ew _____
2.		_____ ui _____
3.		_____ ui _____
4.		_____ ou _____
5.		_____ ou _____
6.		_____ ew _____
7.		_____ ew _____

Read, write, and X it.

1.	trombone _____			
2.	bluebells _____			
3.	notebook _____			
4.	baboon _____			
5.	sawdust _____			
6.	jewel _____			
7.	flounder _____			

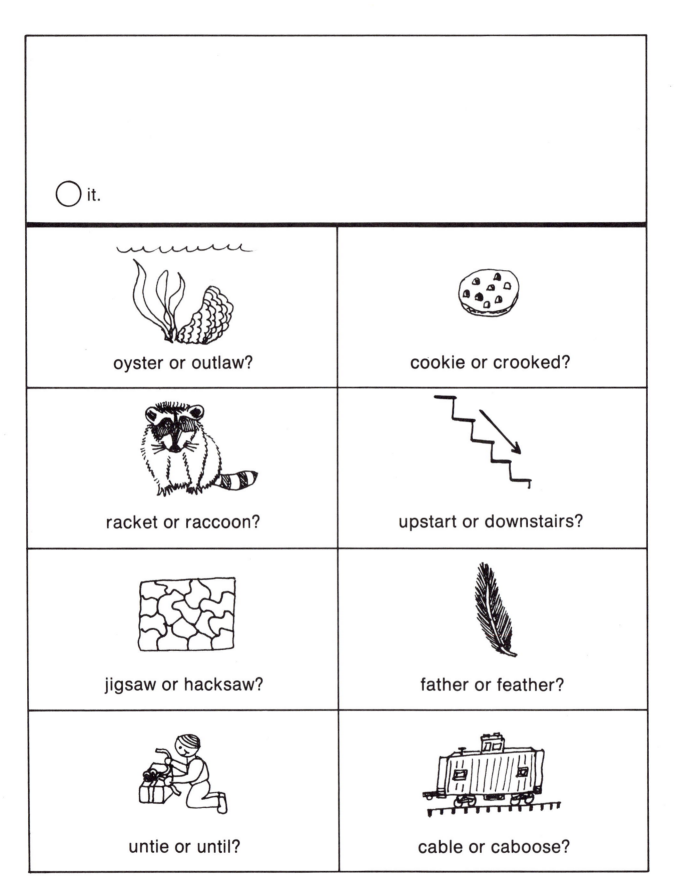

◯ it.

oyster or outlaw?

cookie or crooked?

racket or raccoon?

upstart or downstairs?

jigsaw or hacksaw?

father or feather?

untie or until?

cable or caboose?

	Spell.		Write.
1.	saw sow	dust desk	_____
2.	nout note	bute book	_____
3.	rac raic	coon cone	_____
4.	ow oy	ster ters	_____
5.	coot cook	ie oy	_____
6.	pret prew	zel tel	_____
7.	snaw snow	flack flake	_____

Yes or no?

		Yes	No
1.	Will a broken cookie crumble into bits?	☐	☐
2.	Can a brass trombone be used to blow sweet music?	☐	☐
3.	Can a raccoon finish a jigsaw puzzle?	☐	☐
4.	Can you eat oyster stew with a teaspoon?	☐	☐
5.	Are tasty pretzels made out of sawdust?	☐	☐
6.	If you untie the ropes of a cruise ship, will it float away?	☐	☐
7.	Can a baboon print its name on its homework and notebooks?	☐	☐

blue jay bluefish blueberry	lightheaded lightning lighthouse
barber barefoot barnstorm	boomerang bookcase bookmark
cracker barrel crockery crocodile	forward firewood fireworks
clout county cloudy	moustache mouse hole mustard
igloo unglue ignoble	destiny destroy deserve

Pick the best word to finish each sentence.

countdown	sawdust	sirloin
rooster	raccoon	igloo
barefoot	argue	shampoo

1. At dawn you can hear the _____ crowing.

2. When the lumberjack cuts wood with a chainsaw, the pile of _____ grows high.

3. An _____ is an ice house.

4. When your teacher tells you to begin your work, you must not _____.

5. Before the astronauts blast off, they will begin the _____.

6. It is such fun to go _____ on the warm, sandy beach.

7. When I wash my hair, I use _____ that smells like flowers.

X it.

1. Jason is happy sauntering in the mud with his bare feet. ☐

   Staggering barefoot in the woods, Jason began to cry. ☐

2. The crazy raccoon is pretending to be a cowhand. ☐

   The outlaw is trying to play with the raccoon's toys. ☐

3. The prowler will unhook the barnyard gate to free the roosters. ☐

   The president's navy blue necktie has a rooster on it. ☐

4. Rosemary is grilling sirloins on the barbecue. ☐

   Barbara is shaking hands with her new friend, Sir James Lion. ☐

5. Homer is shampooing his black retriever. ☐

   Homer's retriever is taking a snooze on the couch. ☐

6. Raymond is catching flounder in a frying pan. ☐

   Raymond is flying south with a flounder under his arm. ☐

7. Andy is in the park ready to enjoy a pretzel from the pretzel wagon. ☐

   The baboon has hot pretzels and soup for lunch. ☐

Write it.

1.	_____
2.	_____
3.	_____
4.	_____
5.	_____
6.	_____
7.	_____

Book 6 — Posttest

Circle the 2 words in each box that have the same vowel sound.

1.	frown couch stoop	2.	field teach boast
3.	blest green spread	4.	skirt glide slight
5.	moist oyster mouse	6.	shield churn third
7.	throat stoop flew	8.	shows groans blooms
9.	world snort churn	10.	thread chain paste
11.	fault train drawn	12.	fruit bloat gloom

Book 6 — Posttest

(Teacher dictated. See Key for Books 6, 7, 8.)

1.	squeaking swarming squirting scorching squirming	2.	squawking sprawling sauntering sparkler spareribs
3.	powerfully pound cake powdery powerless poverty	4.	cheating chieftain chiefly cheapen cheesy
5.	frightening fricassee frightfulness friendless fretfulness	6.	withstand withhold withers witching withdrew
7.	northwest northwards northerly northeaster northlander	8.	pheasant peasant pleasant plentiful planets
9.	harpooned hairpinned happened harpsichord harmony	10.	undertook undercooked understock understood understudy

Book 6 — Posttest

(Teacher dictated. See Key for Books 6, 7, 8.)

1. _____

_____

2. _____

_____

3. _____

_____

4. _____

_____

5. _____

_____

6. _____

_____

Book 6 — Posttest

Use the words to complete the sentences.

beach	foot	moonlit
shark	surf	sunburn
straw	necktie	proudly

1. On a _____ night, Paul was swimming in the roaring _____ . Suddenly he saw a monster gliding underneath his _____ . It was a _____ with long, sharp teeth. The sight of that monster sent Paul quickly back to sit on the sandy _____ .

_____

burning	outdoors	lightning
warning	fireworks	tightrope
burning	corner	handlebar

2. Without _____ there was a loud Bang! Zap! Crackle! Bang! Howdy rushed _____ to see if _____ had struck the barn or if the house next door was _____ . The night sky was bright with dazzling light and showers of sparks. However, it was just the _____ display.

_____

trout	barefoot	sight
worms	round	thread
sneakers	raccoon	broomstick

3. Rachel woke very early in the morning, grabbed her sweater, and scampered into the field to dig a cupful of _____ . Rapidly she ran to the brook where she took off her _____ . She waded _____ into the water with her rod and reel. Soon the skillful girl had a _____ on her line. She threw it into a _____ bucket and returned to fish some more. At this point the head of a hungry _____ appeared in the ferns. Will the thief gobble down the fish before Rachel catches sight of the tricky raccoon?